Collins

SCRABBLE
BRAND CROSSWORD GAME

junior

Spelling
Activity book

Age 8-9

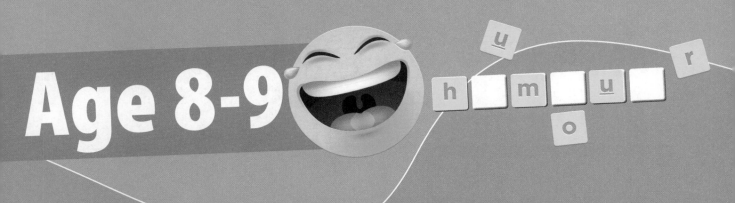

...hed by Collins
...print of HarperCollinsPublishers
...rhill Road
...obriggs
...ow G64 2QT
...harpercollins.co.uk

...rCollinsPublishers
...or, Watermarque Building, Ringsend Road, Dublin 4,
...d

...2 Mattel. SCRABBLE™ and SCRABBLE tiles, including S1
...re trademarks of Mattel.

...s ® is a registered trademark of HarperCollins Publishers
...ed
...collins.co.uk

...ublished in 2022

...rperCollins Publishers 2022

ISBN 978-0-00-852621-4

10 9 8 7 6 5 4 3 2 1

A catalogue record for this book is available from the British Library

Printed in Great Britain by Martins the Printers

If you would like to comment on any aspect of this book, please contact us at the above address or online.

E-mail: dictionaries@harpercollins.co.uk

f facebook.com/collinsdictionary
y @collinsdict

ACKNOWLEDGEMENTS
All images © Shutterstock.com

FUN JUMBLES

Unscramble these words, then add the endings -ing and -ed.
Remember to make any spelling adjustments!
The first one has been done for you.

i m t l i

l i m i t i n g

l i m i t e d

l e i k c t

d e p a l

r e f s r a n t

These words don't have the ending 'ed' when written in the past tense. Can you write the correct spellings?

b u y ☐ ☐ ☐ ☐ ☐ ☐ ☐

c a t c h ☐ ☐ ☐ ☐ ☐ ☐

e a t ☐ ☐ ☐

WORD FILLS

Add the ending 'ation' to the words and then fill in the crossword. The first one has been done for you.

sense	create	adore	agitate
indicate	limit	found	tempt
fix	prepare	imitate	

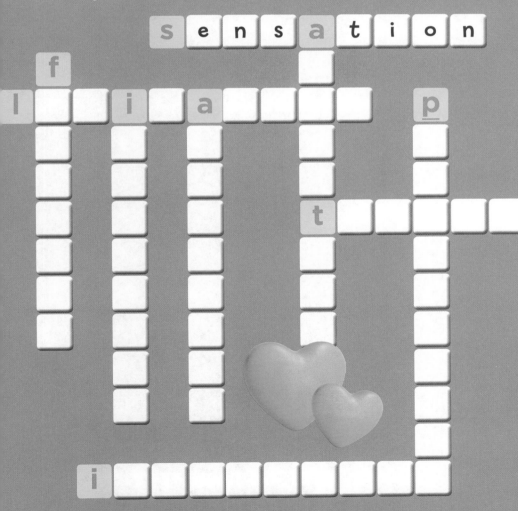

s e n s a t i o n

3

WHY OH Y?

The missing words all contain the letter 'y'. Can you work out what they are?

Check out my new **h a i r s t y l e** .

A **c** ☐ **l** ☐ ☐ ☐ **r** has three faces and two edges.

Mountaineering is a strenuous **p h** ☐ ☐ ☐ ☐ ☐ **l** activi

Egypt is famous for its **p** ☐ ☐ ☐ ☐ ☐ ☐ **s** .

Humans, animals and plants cannot live without **o** ☐ ☐ ☐ ☐ ☐

We were invited for tea in the **r** ☐ ☐ ☐ ☐ palace.

4

PICTURE CLUES

Use the letters oppossite to make four words that contain the letter 'y'. You can use each letter twice. The pictures are clues to help you.

CLUE SOLVER

Fill in the blank spaces to solve the clues.

Strange or puzzling
m _ _ _ _ _ _ _ _ _ s

A percussion instrument
c _ _ _ _ _ l

A traditional story that was made up or misleading
m _ _ _

A type of snake
p _ _ _ _ _

5

PERFECT MATCH

Match the first half of each word on the left, to the second half on the right. The first one has been done for you.

a n t i	m a r i n e
i n t e r	l e g a l
s u b	s o c i a l
s u p e r	s o n i c
a u t o	m o r t a l
i l	a c t i o n
i r	r e g u l a r
i m	g r a p h

MISSING BEGINNINGS

The first parts of these words are missing. Can you guess what they are?

		r e s p o n s i b l e
		s e p t i c
		p i l o t
		c i t y
		w o m a n
	p e r f e c t

MATCH THE MEANING

The beginning of some words have a meaning. Do you know what these words mean? Match each to the correct definition.

a n t i   among or between

a u t o   against

s u b   self or own

i n t e r   under

s u p e r   very good, excellent

UNJUMBLE

Unjumble the letters to make words ending in 'sure' or 'ture'.

e a e t r u̲ s r

p̲ t u̲ i r c e

a s̲ u e r e m

u̲ n t c r u̲ e p̲

e r u̲ n̲ i t f u̲ r

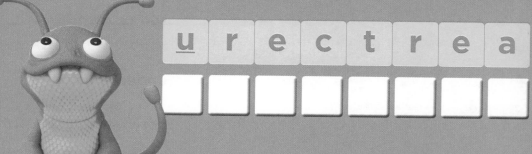

u̲ r e c t r e a

LETTER SHUFFLE

Unscramble the letters in the circles, then write them in the boxes below to make words ending in -ous.

Change each noun into an adjective by adding the ending -ous. You might want to use a dictionary to help you with the spelling.

c o u r a g e

v i g o u r

h u m o u r

MAKING ADVERBS

Add the ending -ly to turn these adjectives into adverbs. One has been done for you.

beautiful   musical   careful
suspicious   definite   merry
lucky   cheeky
calm   dramatic

c h e e k i l y

b

m

m

s

d

l

c

c

d

CROSSWORD CLUES

Use the clues to fill in the crossword with adverbs connected to actions. Watch out – there is one trick answer!

How you write if you are neat.

How you act if you are cautious.

How you respond if you are grateful.

How you drink if you are thirsty.

How you eat if you are hungry.

How you eat if you are greedy.

How you run if you are fast.

How you shout if you are angry.

AY, AY, AY!

Write the missing letters to complete each word. All the words have an 'ay' sound spelt either 'ei', 'eigh' or 'ey'.

o b e y

w ☐ ☐ ☐ ☐

b ☐ ☐ g e

r ☐ ☐ n

r ☐ ☐ g n

☐ ☐ ☐ ☐

p r ☐ ☐

s l ☐ ☐ ☐ ☐

g r ☐ ☐

FUN JUMBLES

The letters of the words on page 12 have been jumbled up. Unscramble them, then fill in the crossword.

ROGUE WORDS!

Words with the ending -gue are tricky to spell. The clues and pictures will help you to find words that end with these letters. Use a dictionary to help you.

Tip: Fill in the word endings first

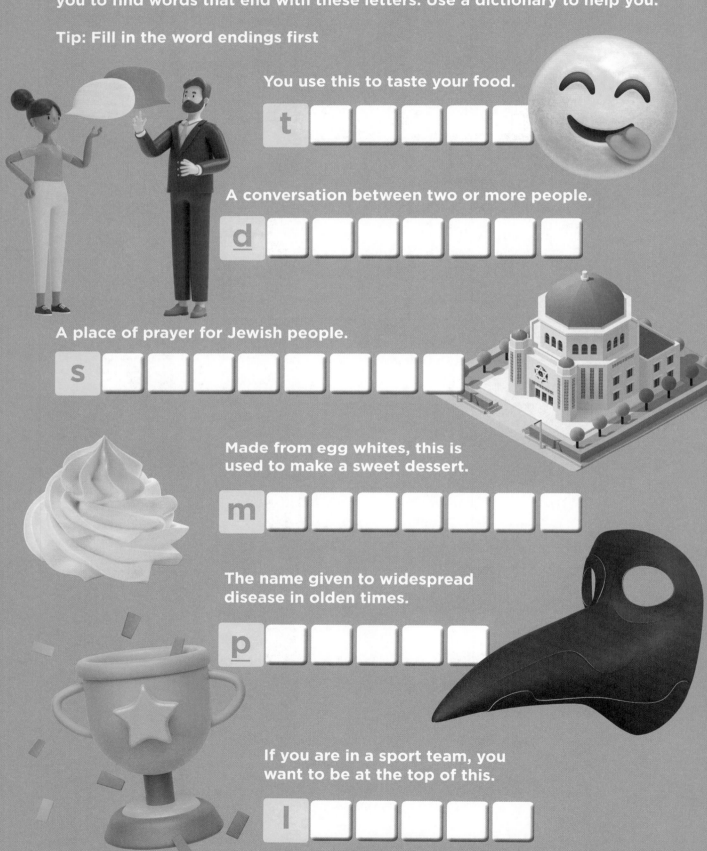

You use this to taste your food.

t ⬚ ⬚ ⬚ ⬚ ⬚

A conversation between two or more people.

d̲ ⬚ ⬚ ⬚ ⬚ ⬚ ⬚ ⬚

A place of prayer for Jewish people.

s ⬚ ⬚ ⬚ ⬚ ⬚ ⬚ ⬚ ⬚

Made from egg whites, this is used to make a sweet dessert.

m ⬚ ⬚ ⬚ ⬚ ⬚ ⬚ ⬚

The name given to widespread disease in olden times.

p̲ ⬚ ⬚ ⬚ ⬚ ⬚

If you are in a sport team, you want to be at the top of this.

l ⬚ ⬚ ⬚ ⬚

14

IMPROVE YOUR SPELLING

Similarly, when the letters 'que' come at the end of a word, you don't say them as you'd expect. Can you unscramble the words and write them correctly? Use the clues and a dictionary to help you. Tip: The letter 'q' is always followed by the letter 'u'.

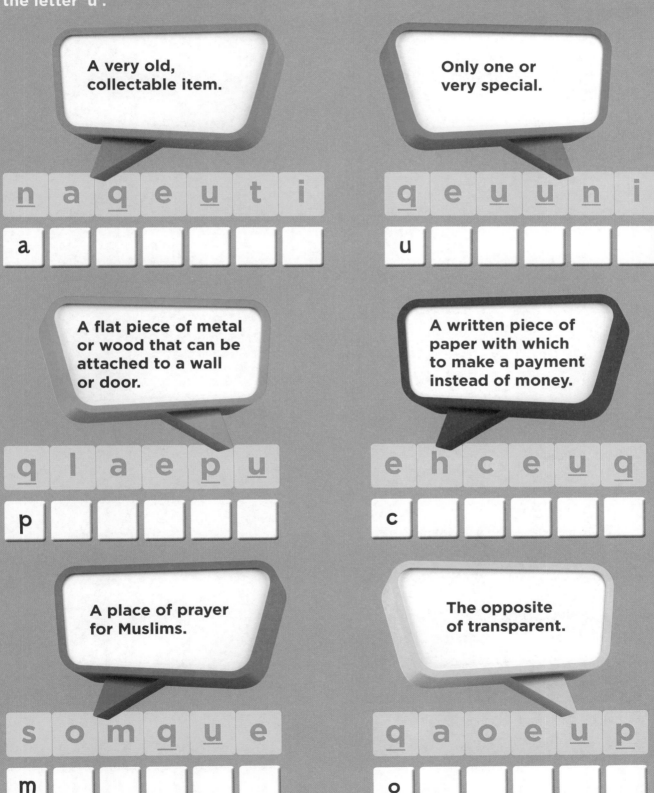

A very old, collectable item.

n a q e u t i

a ☐ ☐ ☐ ☐ ☐ ☐

Only one or very special.

q e u u n i

u ☐ ☐ ☐ ☐ ☐

A flat piece of metal or wood that can be attached to a wall or door.

q l a e p u

p ☐ ☐ ☐ ☐ ☐

A written piece of paper with which to make a payment instead of money.

e h c e u q

c ☐ ☐ ☐ ☐ ☐

A place of prayer for Muslims.

s o m q u e

m ☐ ☐ ☐ ☐ ☐

The opposite of transparent.

q a o e u p

o ☐ ☐ ☐ ☐ ☐

PROPER NOUNS

In each column below, there are 7 words that should begin with a capital letter. The first letter of each one spells something nice to eat! Write the tasty treat in the tiles at the bottom of each column.

egg	brandon	lemon
patrick	vinegar	leg
apple	dance	carla
oliver	ireland	label
pacific	nail	rug
tractor	sunday	amazon
canada	cushion	rahid
olivia	purple	august
rabbit	chloe	mercur
rome	uganda	hand
neptune	issac	everes
hamster	tuesday	london

WORDSEARCH

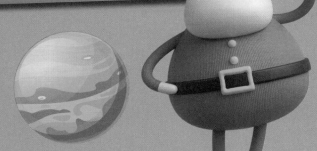

The proper nouns listed below are hidden in the wordsearch. Can you find them all?

z	i	v	s	b	q	c	c	o	d
r	p	y	p	j	w	h	h	m	f
c	b	p	a	a	j	r	e	a	r
y	a	m	i	p	u	i	s	t	i
v	d	n	n	a	n	s	h	t	d
e	l	u	a	n	e	t	i	h	a
n	t	n	b	d	k	m	r	e	y
u	s	k	t	l	a	a	e	w	a
s	t	g	m	e	i	s	y	s	n
b	h	u	d	w	b	n	n	k	o

Canada	Friday	Spain
Cheshire	Japan	Venus
Christmas	June	
Dublin	Matthew	

17

SOUNDS THE SAME

Some words sound the same but are spelt differently. Can you unscramble the words below, then write the word that sounds like it but has a different spelling?

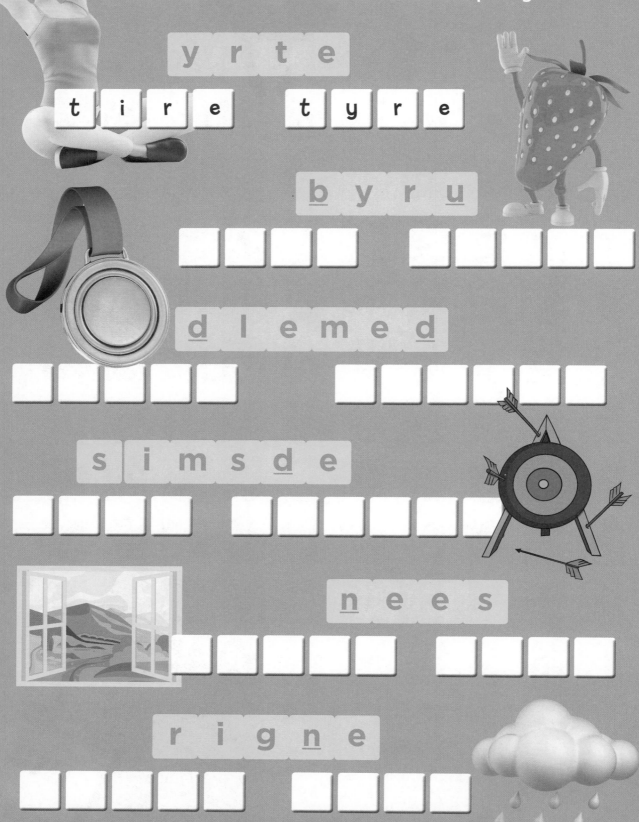

y r t e

t i r e   t y r e

b y r u

d l e m e d

s i m s d e

n e e s

r i g n e

c e a p <u>p</u> e

r o g a <u>n</u>

GIVE US A CLUE

Use the picture clues to help you complete one of each pair of words that sound the same but are spelt differently. Then write the word that sounds the same but has a different spelling. One has been done for you.

<u>b</u> a l l

b a w l

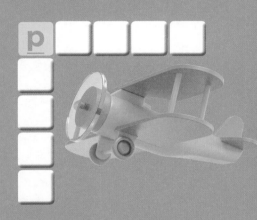

p

m

r

m

f   r

s
t

t h   w

19

ROUNDABOUTS

Unscramble the words with endings that sound like 'shun'. This sound is spelt either -tion, -cian, -sion or -ssion. The first letter of each word is highlighted and will help you fill in the missing letters on the opposite page.

-tion

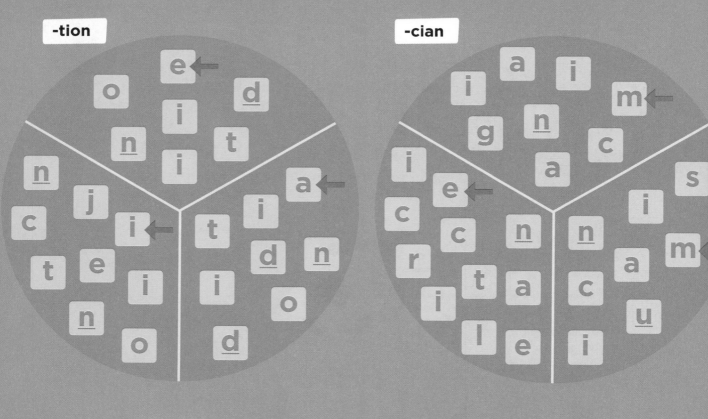

-cian

-ssion

MISSING LETTERS

Tip: fill in the endings first so you don't
have to unscramble as many letters!

'SH' SOUNDS SPELT CH

Unscramble the 4 groups of letters to fill in the blank tiles with words that have a 'sh' sound spelt ch.

m a

i e

n

c h [ ] [ ][ ] [ ][ ]

c

h

a e

t l

p a

u r

a t

e

[ ][ ][ ][ ] c h [ ][ ][ ]

c

h

b

e o

r u

r

'K' SOUNDS SPELT CH

Use the clues to complete the crossword with words that have a 'k' sound spelt ch.

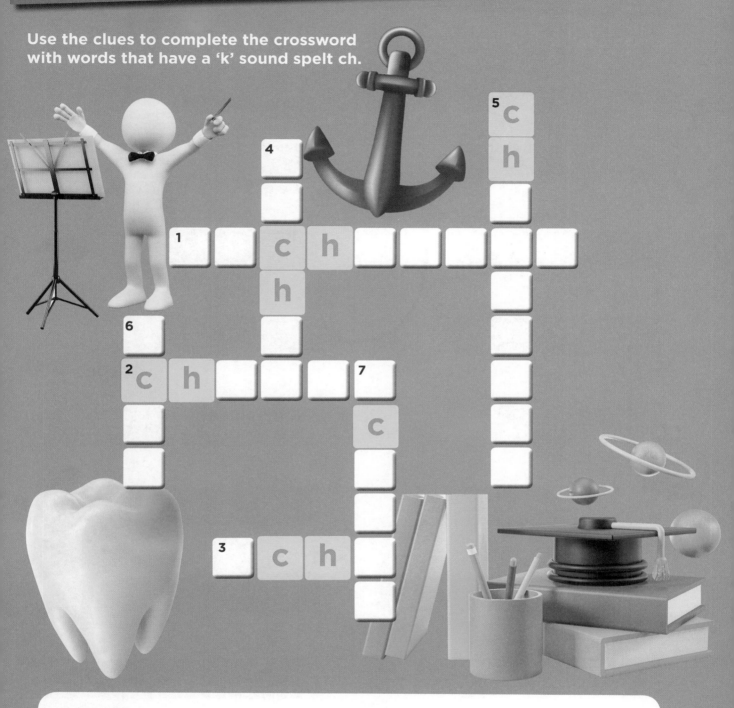

ACROSS

1. A group of musicians.

2. A group of people singing together or lines repeated in a song.

3. A sound repeated, e.g. when you shout in a tunnel.

DOWN

4. You drop this in the water to keep a boat in a particular place.

5. A person in a story, film or play.

6. A pain.

7. A place where you can learn.

COLLECTIVE NOUNS

Can you link each collective noun with its jumbled pair on the right? One has been done for you.

b u **n** c h	o w r e s f l
s w a r m	h e e **p** s
f l o c k	**p** r a g s e
	grapes
a r m y	**d** s f r e i **n**
l i t t e r	s e e **b**
b o **u** **q** **u** e t	s h e **n**
c i r c l e	**p** i e **p** **u** **p** s
b r o o **d**	s t a **n**

24

s h o a l

o l v e s w

b a s k e t

s h i f

p a c k

i o n s l

p r i d e

r u f i t

I CAN SEA YOU!

Write the unjumbled words you've found in the grid, then find another collective noun which runs vertically down the middle that you might see at sea!

f ☐ ☐ ☐ ☐

w ☐ ☐ ☐ ☐ ☐

b ☐ ☐ ☐ ☐

g ☐ ☐ ☐ e ☐

a ☐ ☐ ☐

f ☐ ☐ ☐ ☐ ☐

f ☐ ☐ ☐

f ☐ ☐ ☐ ☐ ☐ ☐ ☐

s h ☐ ☐ ☐

l ☐ ☐ ☐

p ☐ ☐ ☐

h ☐ ☐ ☐

25

2-LETTER WORDS

When you join two words that read across, like two and fox, you have to make sure that the 2 letters reading down make a proper word, i.e. of. Use the letters in the circles to make new words, but always make sure that the 2 letters reading down are proper words!

Now make new joining words with
two 2-letter words reading down.

e

t

t   n

b e a m

m e a t

t   m

o   n

o   h

p   e

o   r   o r

m o o d

a   d

o   t

t   h i s

s o f a

c e

o   r   f

a

f   m e t a l

o   m

d o o r

g   l

o   a

e

m   a   n

a

l e m o n

Now overlap with three 2-letter words!

h

t

o   w a

s   s t o p

o   n

g r e e n

27

CROSSWORD

Use the clues below to solve the crossword. Then unscramble the letters in the marked squares to find something you might use to plan your year!

Mr Noah Balfour
3 Saint Mary Street
Duncanville

ML3 9XP

ACROSS

3. The opposite to well-behaved.

4. You might ride this to school.

6. Half of a half.

9. Smaller than a seventh.

10. The collective noun for apples and oranges.

12. An area of land surrounded by water.

DOWN

1. One hundred years.

2. A measure of how strong you are.

4. What you do when you take a breath in and out.

5. A place where you can borrow books.

7. The place where you live.

8. The period of time when a king or queen rules a country.

11. Someone who protects someone from danger.

GAMES TO PLAY

Chains

Make words that run round the yellow lines opposite. Each word must begin with the last letter of the word before. Take it in turns with a friend!

e g g r i p e a c h

Starwords

Start by putting a word on the board across the middle star square. Then carry on joining words to make a crossword.

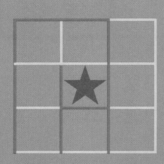

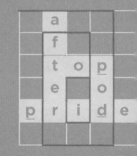

Towers

Put down a 3-letter word. Then cover one letter with a new letter to make a new word. See how high you can make your piles of letters, always making a proper new word.

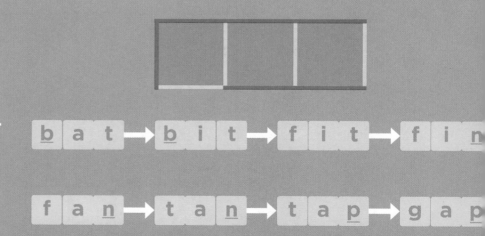

b a t → b i t → f i t → f i n

f a n → t a n → t a p → g a p

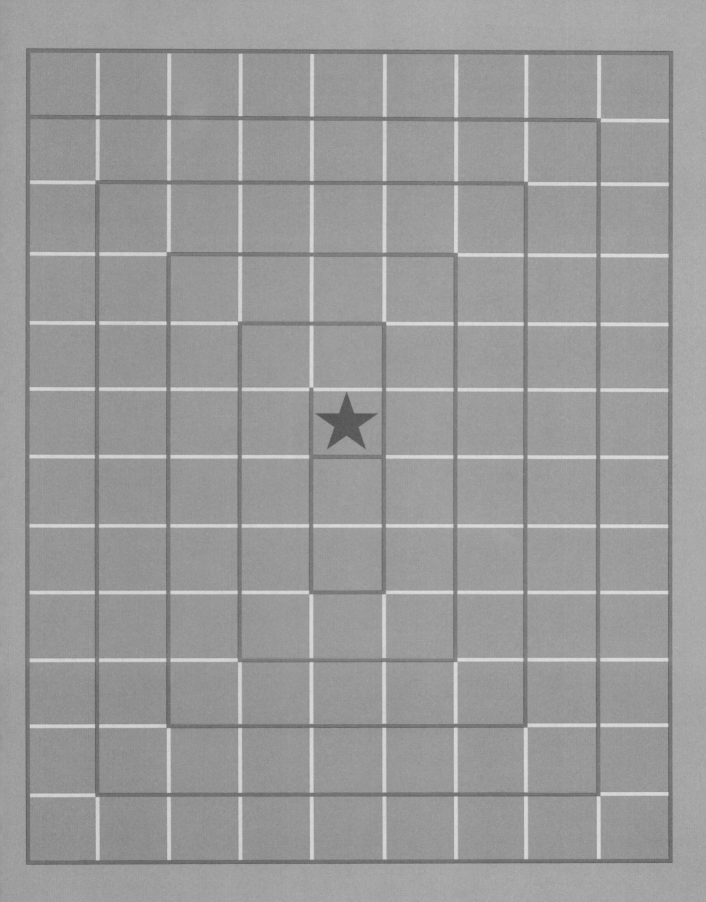

ANSWERS

Page 2
tickle, tickling, tickled
pedal, pedalling, pedalled
transfer, transferring, transferred

Page 3
bought, caught, ate

Page 4
cylinder, physical, pyramids, oxygen, royal

Page 5
type, prayer, tyre, gymnast

mysterious, cymbal, myth, python

Page 6
interaction, submarine, supersonic, autograph, illegal, irregular, immortal

Page 7
irresponsible, antiseptic, autopilot, intercity, superwoman, imperfect

anti – against
auto – self or own
sub – under
inter – among or between
super – very good, excellent

Page 8
treasure, picture, measure, puncture, furniture, creature

Page 9
dangerous, enormous, poisonous, various

courageous, vigorous, humorous

Page 10
beautifully, merrily, musically, suspiciously, dramatically, luckily, calmly, carefully, definitely

Page 11
'fast' is the tricky one
– you can't run 'fastly'!

Page 12
weigh, beige, rein, reign, eight, prey, sleigh grey

Page 13

Page 14
tongue, dialogue, synagogue, meringue, plague, league

Page 15
antique, unique, plaque, cheque, mosque, opaque

Page 16
Patrick, Oliver, Pacific, Canada, Olivia, Rome, Neptune = popcorn

Brandon, Ireland, Sunday, Chloe, Uganda, Isaac, Tuesday = biscuit

Carla, Amazon, Rahid, August, Mercury, Everest, London = caramel

Page 17

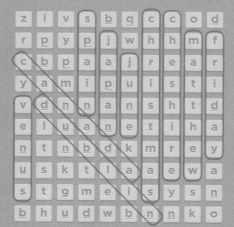

Pages 18–19
bury, berry; medal, meddle; mist, missed; scene, seen; reign, rain/rein; peace, piece; groan, grown

Page 19
plane, plain; meat, meet; road, rode; mail, male; flour, flower; stairs, stares; throw, through

Page 21
-tion
edition, addition, injection
-cian
magician, musician, electrician
-ssion
procession, expression, discussion

Page 22
machine; chalet; brochure; parachute

Page 23

Pages 24–25
swarm of bees; flock of sheep; army of ants; litter of puppies; bouquet of flowers; circle of friends; brood of hens; shoal of fish; basket of fruit; pack of wolves; pride of lions

Page 25

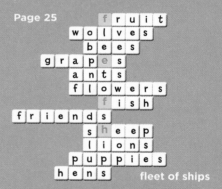

fleet of ships

Page 26
bed: do – owl; tow: we – elf; frog: go – oven; snow: we – ever; tea: as – sum; each: he – bath; mat: am – pea; even: be – crab

Page 27
meat: am – to – month; beam: at – me – tent; mood: or – do – rope; this: if – so – force; sofa: as – do – toad; metal: am – me – foam; door: go – or – goal; lemon: no – an – name; stop: so – to – on – soon; green: we – he – an –

Page 28
ACROSS
3. naughty
4. bicycle
6. quarter
9. eighth
10. fruit
12. island

DOWN
1. century
2. strength
4. breathe
5. library
7. address
8. reign
11. guard

Something to plan your year: calendar